SAFFIYAH'S TALES

MR SHEIK IRFAN HOSSEN KHUDURUN IS A FATHER WHO WISHED TO PURSUE HIS WRITING JOURNEY IN LIGHT OF HIS 4 YEARS OLD DAUGHTER SAFFIYAH. MR SHEIK IRFAN HOSSEN KHUDURUN IS A FURTHER EDUCATION LECTURER AND GAINED EXPERIENCED IN TEACHING RELIGIOUS STUDIES.

By

SHEIK IRFAN HOSSEN KHUDURUN

Contents

Saffiyah and the Rich Man

Once upon a time, there was a little girl named Saffiyah who lived in a very small house with her mum and dad. The house was made up of old timber and covered with a roof made out of straws. Every morning, Saffiyah walks for a long distance to get water from the river as they did not have any water taps in their house. While Saffiyah goes to get water, her father goes to the forest to search for wood to burn as they did not have an oven either!

Saffiyah's mum spends her day cleaning the house and cooking for the family. They were very poor.

One day, a rich man came to Saffiyah's house and mocked at them.

Rich man: "Oh My God! Look at you, your house is so filthy and weak and you don't even have enough water! Ha Ha Ha."

Saffiyah: "We are poor but we are happy."

The rich man did not want to listen to anyone and walked away from the house. As he walked away from the house, disgusted and feeling proud of himself, he suddenly fell down, buckled on his knees and fell in a hole. He cried: "Help! Help! Help!"

The Rich man clothes were ripped and all his belongings were damaged. He continued to cry for help but no one came to his rescue.

The Sun was setting and darkness overpowered the hole.

Saffiyah's father was coming back from the woods and he heard a man crying for help. It was the rich man's desperate cry for help. He put down his stacks of wood and helped the rich man out of the hole. Saffiyah came running to her father and comforted the rich man.

Saffiyah gave the rich man some water, cleaned his clothes and took him to the house.

As the rich man entered the house, he realized how wrong he was by judging Saffiyah's family.

The Rich man apologized to Saffiyah's family for judging them and the next morning he went back to his town.

"Never Judge anyone by the way they look"

Saffiyah and her friend Salaama

Saffiyah was a little girl living with her mother and father in a small wooden house and would go to school every day. She was very poor and had only one pair of slippers, one dress and one toy. Saffiyah spent her whole day playing with her toy – a small white marble. She wakes up every morning, brushed her teeth and washed her face with clean water.

One day, on the way to school, Saffiyah met Salaama, a small girl who went to the same school as her. They started talking.

"Wow, look at your dress Salaama, it's so beautiful", exclaimed Saffiyah.

"Thank You, I got it as a gift," replied Salaama.

Saffiyah stayed quiet and pondered over Salaamas' words. She thought to herself, why does she not receive any gifts. As Saffiyah walked with her pink slippers on the pavement, she muttered to herself: "Why don't I have a nice dress like this? No one gives me any gifts, I don't have anything and I am poor. Salaama's life is so much better than mine!"

Saffiyah mustered some courage and asked her parents for gifts and nice dresses.

Her father was an old man and said to Saffiyah: "My Dear, we have everything that we need and you have clothes to wear."

Saffiyah was not happy and kept complaining and mentioned to her parents about her friend Salaama who had everything and gets a lot of gifts. Saffiyah's father decided to take Saffiyah and went to Salaama's house to see her.

Upon arriving at Salaama's house, Saffiyah was shocked and her face turned pale. She could not believe what she saw!

Salaama was lonely and did not have any parents. She lived in a tent and was cooking her own food. People were coming to her house and dropping food, unwanted clothes to her. Salaama lived a lonely life without a mother and a father. Saffiyah urged her father to help Salaama and her father happily agreed.

On the way back home, Saffiyah had a humble smile on her face and thanked the Lord for blessing her with her parents and everything that she has. Salaama and Saffiyah stayed friends for a lifetime and always helped each other.

"*Appreciate what you have as others may not be as fortunate as you are.*"

Saffiyah and the Three Pots

Saffiyah was very upset and thought that there is nothing to do in life. She was bored and was tired sitting at home or going to school. She came to her mother and asked for advice as to what is it that she can do.

Saffiyah's mother asked her to bring three pots and asked Saffiyah to fill the three pots. Once the three pots were filled with water, Saffiyah was asked to put them on fire until the water starts boiling.

Saffiyah waited and waited and waited. Suddenly she saw steam coming out from the three pots. Saffiyah's mother then brought 3 items. She got one egg, one carrot and some tea bags.   Saffiyah's mum then asked Saffiyah to put each item in one pot while the water was boiling. Saffiyah was very confused but obeyed her mother's instructions.

After few minutes, Saffiyah's mother asked Saffiyah to peel the egg, crush the carrot and take the tea bags out. Saffiyah obeyed her mother but she was very confused!

Saffiyah: "Mum, why did you ask me to do this?"

Saffiyah's mother: "Each of the item was in the same boiling water and boiled for the same amount of time! But look at how each of them reacted?"

Saffiyah's mum explained: "The egg was so soft but now it has become hard. The Carrot was so hard and now it has become soft while the tea bags changed the whole color of the water!"

Saffiyah's mother gently hugged Saffiyah and exclaimed: "Whenever we are in any situation, it is important for us to know how to react. Now, are you an egg, a carrot or the tea bags?"

"We have a choice how to react in difficult situations, think before we Act."

Saffiyah, the Generous Girl

Saffiyah and her father used to cook food and distribute it to poor people who did not have clothes and shelter. Every Friday, Saffiyah would accompany her mother to the market to buy vegetables.

At home, Saffiyah would help her mother preparing the food and in the evening Saffiyah would eagerly accompany her father to distribute it. Saffiyah would put the rice in a small plastic box, sprinkle some onions and put one piece of chicken on top. She would warm the food and then go with her father looking for poor people.

One day, Saffiyah came across a little boy and gave him the food. The little boy did not speak but took the food and ran away. Saffiyah was lost in thoughts!

After many years, Saffiyah now became a grown up girl but her father was very ill. Her father suddenly fell down the stairs and was admitted to the hospital. He needed urgent treatment which cost a lot of money but Alas! Saffiyah did not have any money. There was no one she could ask for help. She tried speaking to the doctor but could not find him either. She stayed in the hospital and cried the whole night!

In the morning, Saffiyah went in her father's room in the hospital and found a note next to her father's table bed.

The note said, "Treatment has been successful and with all bills paid." She was so happy and cried out of happiness. She then felt a touch on her shoulders and a man appeared in front of her. It was the Doctor!

The Doctor said: "I am the same person whom you gave rice when I was small. I was homeless and I did not have any food, today I got the chance to treat your father as a thankful gesture. You gave me food when I was hungry and I am grateful and today I treated your father for free."

Saffiyah cried in happiness and thanked the Lord for his favor.

"Every Good Deed is rewarded."

Saffiyah's Palace

Once upon a time, there was a King who wanted to buy a house for himself as he loved beautiful things. He went to town to find the best house but he could not find anything. So he made a plan with his friend and announced it to the whole town:

"Whoever makes the most beautiful house, I will buy it and offer any price that the seller wants and you all have two days to get this done!" the King announced.

Saffiyah wanted the king to buy her house. She quickly ran home, and started cleaning her house. First she cleaned the kitchen, then the living room and all the

18

windows, the doors, the floor and the roof. For two days, she kept cleaning and cleaning her house.

On the other side of the town, there was a man named Tim who also had a big house. He was too lazy to clean his house and decided to paint over his dirty house. He worked continuously for two days painting his house with different colors.

Two days were over and the King came back to buy his house. First he looked at Tim's house. He was exalted to see Tim's house. It was beautiful. The whole house was painted with glittering colors and pearls. The House had different colors and the King was impressed and decided to buy Tim's house. But then he thought, "Let me see Saffiyah's house as well."

The king travelled to Saffiyah's house and as he arrived, he could not believe his eyes!

It was noon and the sun rays reflected on Saffiyah's house. It was miraculous. The wall reflected with glistening colors of the rainbow and the beautiful colors of the sky. The windows and doors were so clean that it looked like mirrors which brightened the house. Saffiyah's house looked like a palace and all the colors surrounding the house reflected on it. The King was struck in awe!!

Immediately, he bought Saffiyah's house as it was so clean and smelled like roses. It was the best house he had ever seen in his life as it was so clean. He named it Saffiyah's Palace!

"Cleanliness is half of faith. Wipe away all sins and your heart will be clean and pure."

Saffiyah and Her Fortune Search

As the Sun smiled through the white drapes onto Saffiyah's face, her brown eyes opened looking at the white ceiling. Saffiyah stretched her arms and legs and was thankful to the Almighty Lord for giving her another day to live.   She knew this new morning was going to be different, but how?

Saffiyah entered her new dress and heard her mother's sweet voice in the living room.

Saffiyah's mother was upset and was looking at pictures of destitute children in poor countries. In the blink of an eye, Saffiyah's face shined with hope and excitement as she got a wonderful idea!

Saffiyah: "Mum, I got an idea!!!! Let's help them, let's give them clothes, food, water, a new house!!"

Saffiyah's mum replied: "My sweet daughter, this is a very good idea! This intention is called Charity. Giving in charity is a noble act and it does not decrease you in wealth but increases you in wealth."

Saffiyah got even more excited and decided to give everything she had in charity so she is able to get more money and further give even more in Charity.

Saffiyah shouted: "The Whole world's poverty will end!!! YYyyAAAyyyyyyyy!"

Saffiyah embarked on a journey of finding her money. She looked underneath her bed...Then in her cupboard... Over the shelf... In the kitchen... Under her pillows... In her purse... In her books... Underneath the pots in the living room...

Finally she found it!!! It was £5.00 and she exclaimed to herself: "That's it!!!! With £5.00 I will get more and then I will be able to give more. And more poor people will be helped."

She rushed to her mother and jumped in her lap and handed her the £5.00 and asked her mother to donate the £5.00 towards the poor people.

Suddenly a loud noise was heard. The door creaked open and Saffiyah's father appeared.

Saffiyah's father:

"Safffffiiiyyaaaahhhhh, please come and take your gift. I have got you a £10 note and you can buy anything you want with it!"

Saffiyah: "Oh my goodness, Yes Yes Yes Yes Yes, that's it!! I can help the poor. I gave £5.00 and I got more straight away!!!!"

Eventually Saffiyah kept increasing in wealth and she helped so many poor and destitute in the community and her search for fortune to help the world never ended!!

"Always give Charity as it does not decrease you in wealth but increase you in wealth and help overcome poverty"

Saffiyah's Discovery

It was middle of the year, and the world was in a pandemic called Covid-19. It was a scary time and the only way to decrease the spread of the Pandemic was to stay at home.

Saffiyah was waiting for the last day of staying at home as she wanted to go out and play with her friends. But she was bored at home! She kept looking at the trees dancing to the sound of the wind outside, the branches swinging left and right and the leaves rustling on the ground. It was like an orchestra of nature waiting for the pandemic to be over.

Saffiyah did not like the way she was. Her arms were hurting, her legs became numb and her body was asking for fun and frolic.

Saffiyah: "It is tooo boring, I have nowhere to go! My arms and legs are useless as I can't run outside or play with my toys with my friends!"

After couple of days, the Pandemic was over and everyone was able to go out. Saffiyah's mother took her to her workplace.

Saffiyah was excited to meet new people. She always love seeing new people and meeting everyone. She loved talking!! But this time something different was about to happen!

As Saffiyah made her baby steps at her mother's workplace. She saw three boys.

They were all on a wheelchair. They could not talk, they could not eat and their hands and feet were not able to move. Saffiyah was emotional.

Saffiyah: "Bilal, Eeemaan and Hamza are my friends from now and I will help them being happier. I can move my arms and hands but they can't... I will play with them."

Saffiyah discovered her new friends and realized that she should be grateful that she has got arms and legs that are fully healthy and said sorry to herself for thinking they were useless. Her new discovery of Bilal, Eeemaan and Hamza made her more grateful and realized her new friends are heavenly sent, which she will be cherishing for life.

"Everyone is special in their own way. Be grateful and content with everything you have been blessed with."